Dick King-Smith

Omnibombulator

Illustrated by Jim and Peter Kavanagh

YOUNG CORGI

OMNIBOMBULATOR
A YOUNG CORGI BOOK 978 0 552 56740 4

First published in Great Britain by Doubleday,
an imprint of Random House Children's Publishers UK
A Random House Group Company

Doubleday edition published 1995
Young Corgi edition published 1996

This edition published 2013

1 3 5 7 9 10 8 6 4 2

The Random House Group Limited supports the Forest Stewardship Council® (FSC®), the leading
international forest-certification organisation. Our books carrying the FSC label are printed
on FSC®-certified paper. FSC is the only forest-certification scheme supported by the leading
environmental organisations, including Greenpeace. Our paper procurement policy
can be found at www.randomhouse.co.uk/environment

Set in Palatino

Young Corgi Books are published by Random House Children's Publishers UK,
61–63 Uxbridge Road, London W5 5SA

www.randomhousechildrens.co.uk
www.randomhouse.co.uk

Addresses for companies within The Random House Group Limited
can be found at: www.randomhouse.co.uk/offices.htm

THE RANDOM HOUSE GROUP Limited Reg. No. 954009

A CIP catalogue record for this book is available from the British Library.

Printed and bound in Great Britain by CPI Group (UK) Ltd, Croydon CR0 4YY

Contents

CHAPTER ONE
The Naming

Omnibombulator was a very small beetle.

He was born small, like all his brothers and sisters, but unlike them he stayed small.

Like them, he had six legs, but his were very little legs and his six feet were of a very small size.

One day his mother, June Beetle, said to his father, whose name was Bert, "Bert."

"Yes, June?" said Bert Beetle.

"What's the longest boy's name you can think of?"

"Why?" said Bert.

"Because," said June Beetle, "we have one extremely small son and I think he

should have a nice long name to make him feel important. So what's the longest one you know?"

Bert thought. After a bit he said,

"I've never heard of that before."
"You wouldn't have. I just made it up."
"'Omnibombulator',' said June Beetle.
"I like it." And she called her very small

son and told him his name.

"Do you think that's a nice name?" she said.

Omnibombulator scratched his very

small head with one of his very small front legs.

"It's a bit long, Mum," he said in his very small voice.

"That's the whole point," said his mother.

"There's never been a beetle with such a long name. Now you'll be important and everyone will take notice of you."

CHAPTER TWO
The Big World

It didn't seem to Omnibombulator that his name made much difference in fact.

Woodlice still pushed him out of the way without so much as a by-your-leave. Earwigs ran over him as though he wasn't there. Snails walked across him and made him all slimy.

Even ladybirds tipped him upside down and left him frantically wiggling his six very small legs in the air.

And, to his many brothers and sisters, he remained extremely unimportant.

"Out of the way, Titch," they would say as they scurried about the garden looking for food, that is if they bothered to notice him at all.

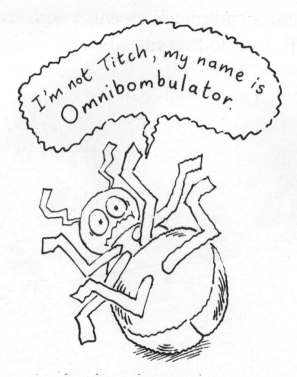

And when he said, "I'm not Titch, my name is Omnibombulator," none of them took a blind bit of notice.

Omnibombulator went, with very small steps, to find his father.

"Dad," he said.

"Yes, Omnibombulator, my boy?" said Bert Beetle, rolling the name round his tongue with pride, for after all he had invented it.

"Mum told me everyone would take notice of me, but they don't," said Omnibombulator.

"Maybe they don't see you," said his father. "After all, you are a bit on the small side. Try saying your name loudly when you meet someone. 'Hullo!' you must shout. 'My name is Omnibombulator!'

"Once they hear that, it'll stop 'em dead in their tracks. What a name, they'll think!

He must be a very important beetle!"

So Omnibombulator tried shouting his name at passers-by but, of course, it was a very small shout and most didn't hear him. The few that did said, "Omni what?" and then hurried away before he could say, ". . . bombulator".

Soon Omnibombulator began to regret having been given such a long name. Mum and Dad were wrong, he said to himself.

It's not going to make me important. I was better off when I didn't have a name. And anyway, I don't really mind being small.

It has its advantages.

And it did, because in the garden were not only woodlice and earwigs and snails and ladybirds, but birds too –

great monsters like blackbirds and thrushes, that ate a lot of the garden creatures, including a great many of Omnibombulator's brothers and sisters.

17

But because he was so small and
unimportant, the birds didn't notice him.
So Omnibombulator gave up shouting
his name at passers-by in his very small
voice and concentrated on staying alive.

As Omnibombulator grew up, he became an orphan, for June and Bert Beetle tragically met a greedy bird one morning.

Omnibombulator could only be glad that in their death they were still together.

And now they're gone, he thought,
there's nothing to keep me here. I'll set out
to see the world and seek my fortune. So
off he set.

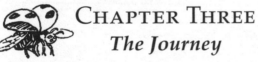 # CHAPTER THREE
The Journey

Because his six little legs were so small,
it took Omnibombulator half a day to
get out of the garden and into a country
lane.

I shan't see much of the world at this rate, he thought. Little did he know that soon he was to travel much faster!

He was making his weary way along the lane as the light was fading, looking for somewhere safe to spend the night, when he saw a strange object under the hedge. It was an old boot, lying on its side.

Omnibombulator did not know what this huge thing was but he thought it looked a good place for a very small beetle to hide in, so he plodded into it and went to sleep.

Next morning he was rudely awakened.

A whiskery tramp had been trudging along the lane, after a night spent under a haystack, when he spied the old boot.

Now if there's one thing a tramp needs, its a good pair of boots, and this tramp had a big hole in his left boot. The right boot was OK but the left one let in water all the time.

And this old boot, the tramp saw with pleasure, was a left one.

But would it fit? He sat down on the grass verge to try it on.

Omnibombulator was shaken violently out of a deep sleep as the tramp picked up the old boot and shoved his foot into it.

Hastily Omnibombulator retreated before the huge advancing toes until he reached the inside of the toecap and could go no further. Desperately he pressed himself against its leather wall.

Because the boot was a fraction too big for the tramp's foot, and because he was very small, Omnibombulator survived.

He was in total darkness, jammed against a very dirty big toe that stuck through a hole in the tramp's sock, and the smell was simply awful.

Now began a journey that was
to take Omnibombulator far far
away from his birthplace. The
boot that had been his refuge
was now his prison and might
indeed have become
his grave, because
the tramp very
seldom took his
boots off.

Omnibombulator became faint with hunger, gassed by the smell of foot, and shaken half to death by the thump thumping as the tramp tramped along.

It's the end for me, he thought. Soon I
shall be once more reunited with Mum
and Dad.

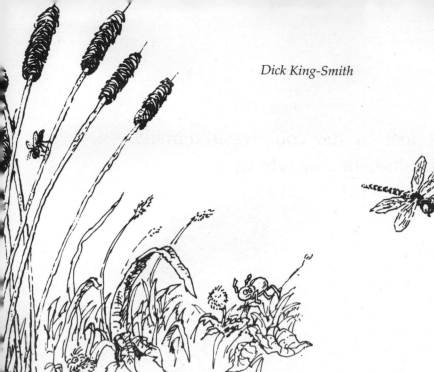

But just then the terrible thumping stopped and the horrible foot was withdrawn from the boot. With the last of his strength Omnibombulator crawled out and wobbled away from the tramp, who was sitting by a river bank, dabbling

his hot feet in the cool water. Finally,
Omnibombulator was safe again.

CHAPTER FOUR
The Homecoming

Once Omnibombulator's very small head cleared and he had filled his very small stomach, he set out again on his six very small legs.

The world, he desided, was much too dangerous a place, and he determined to return to the garden of his birth.

The walk which had taken the tramp a couple of hours took Omnibombulator a week, but at last he reached his goal.

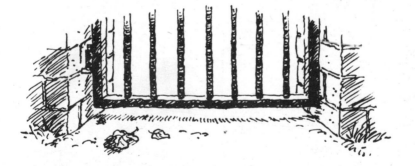

I may be small he thought, and I may be unimportant, but I'm safely home at last.

But even as he was making his way up
the garden path, he heard the beating of
great wings.

He raised his very small head to see the most enormous black-and-white bird swooping down towards him.

As fast as his very small feet could carry him, Omnibombulator made for a crack between the paving stones.

A very small crack it was – much too
small for any of his brothers and sisters
or his late lamented mother and father to
have squeezed into. But Omnibombulator
got down it all right, just as the magpie
landed on the path.

It was pitch dark in the crack between the stones as the bird crouched above, but at last it flew away again and Omnibombulator could see that he was not alone.

Another beetle was hiding there too – a very small beetle, exactly the same size as himself. It must be a baby, he thought.

"Don't be scared, baby," he said. "I'm going to take care of you."

"MY!" said the other very small beetle. "You're a very fast worker! We haven't even been introduced."

Omnibombulator could tell by its voice that it was a she-beetle. He climbed up out of the crack and she followed.

"You're a little girl," he said.
"And you're a little boy," said she.

"Well, yes, I'm not big," said Omnibombulator. "I'll admit that. But you see,
in fact, I'm a grown-up beetle. It's just that
I didn't grow up very far."

"'That's lovely!" cried the she-beetle.

"Because that's just what happened to me.
I'm a grown-up too! I'm just very small,
like you."

How wonderful, thought Omnibombulator. We were made for each other.

"What's your name?" he said.

"I haven't got one," said the very small
she-beetle in her very small voice. "They

never bothered to call me anything.
What's yours?"

Omnibombulator took a deep breath.
This is it, he thought. At last someone is
asking me my name, someone very pretty
and just the right size. Here goes.

He said slowly, "My name is,"

"Oh!" breathed the she-beetle. "Omni-bombulator! With a name like that, you must be a terribly important beetle!" And she rubbed one of her very small front legs on one of his.

"Not really," he said.

"Oh yes, you are," she said. "To me, you're the most important beetle in the world."

The End

❧ ABOUT THE AUTHOR ❧

DICK KING-SMITH was a Gloucestershire farmer until the age of 45, when he gave up farming to become a primary school teacher. His first book, *The Fox Busters*, was published in 1978, and he went on to become a prolific and bestselling full-time author, writing well over a hundred books. His work received many awards, including a Smarties Prize Bronze Medal for *All Because of Jackson* and the Children's Book Award for *Harriet's Hare*, and he was also voted Children's Author of the Year in 1992. His top-selling title *The Sheep-Pig* was developed into the Academy Award nominated movie *Babe*. He passed away in 2011 at the age of 88.

❖ THE ADVENTUROUS SNAIL ❖

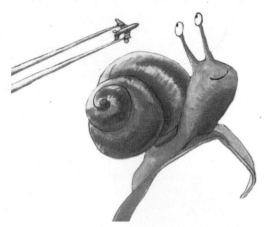

Snail on board!

Siegfried loves to explore. One day his explorations
take him on a big adventure – from his home in the
grass, to the airport, on to an aeroplane and
all the way to America!

There he makes some very important friends,
Mr Ambassador and Mr President, finds a new
home in a sandwich box – and also meets
the lovely Peggy Sue . . .

978 0 552 56741 1

🐾 TITUS RULES OK 🐾

"Titus, my boy," said the Queen, "I have a funny feeling that you are going to be a very special dog."

Titus is a young corgi puppy, growing up in Windsor Castle. There is lots he must learn (like how not to trip up Prince Philip!). Soon he becomes the Queen's favourite, and she even lets him sleep on her bed at night! And it is because of Titus that Her Majesty finally does something very surprising . . .

978 0 552 55431 2